Welsh Slate
Past & Pr

Based on 'Victorian Slate Mining' by the late Ivor Wynne Jones

Compiled by Lindsey Porter

Introduction

In late Victorian times the slate mining industry was largely confined to a few mines in North Wales.

Slate production did not involve a massive amount of capital. Once the rock had been removed to the dressing floor and cut to the required size, it was easily split by hand to the right thickness. Photographs herein show the men sitting with a block of cut stone leaning against their leg. It was a simple job with a hammer and chisel to separate the slates one at a time from the block of stone.

There was not a lot of expensive machinery underground and removal of the slate rock and waste was easily achieved by horse power along levels. In mines with inclined beds of stone it was necessary for the wagons to be hauled by cable up the inclined floor of the workings, to a nearby dressing floor on the hillside above.

Some of the chambers created by the removal of rock are huge, with 86ft (26m) ladders necessary for safety checks of the roof. It was an inherently dangerous occupation, from falling rock and initially primitive means of lifting heavy boulders onto the wagons.

This perception of the danger, lead to a Government Commission into the mines in 1894. The report of the findings was illustrated by the photography of J.C. Burrows, who already enjoyed a reputation for his underground photography in the mines in Cornwall.

His work in North Wales, including additional photography commissioned at Llechwedd, near Blaenau Ffestiniog, has left a clear understanding of what the mines were like and an invaluable record of an industry with which North Wales is indelibly connected.

His photographs show the dependency on the candle for lighting and the almost universal lack of protective helmets for the miners, despite their availability elsewhere in the mining industry at that time.

Today it is possible to quarry the stone much more easily than to mine it and old workings are being uncovered as stone left by the old miners is being removed. The huge tips of waste are being recovered now to provide road-stone and have also become popular as surface cover in gardens.

This book vividly recalls how slate rock was mined and turned into roofing slates all those years ago. It also shows the uses to which slate is now being put in the building industry. Today, creative designs in building development are seeing a renaissance in the use of slate, spearheaded by Llechwedd once more.

At the rear of this book are scenes of Llechwedd today, including examples of the diversity of uses to which this enduring building material is now being used.

The author acknowledges that some of the captions in this book have been drawn, with permission, from 'Victorian Slate Mining' by the late Ivor Wynne Jones, who was associated with the industry for several decades.

Llechwedd Slate Mines

J.W. Greaves commenced extracting slate from the Llechwedd mines early in 1836, taking the raw material from a rich Ordovician deposit laid down around 500 years ago. Since that time the company have built up the reputation of providing high quality blue-grey slate, which has found market places in many corners of the world. Over one hundred and seventy years on, the company remains fiercely independent, producing slate for use throughout the country and within the European market place.

Greaves as a company has the unique accolade of having its own registered trademark 'GREAVES PORTMADOG SLATE' for the product it produces, an honour to set its slate above all other competition.

Being a natural product slight shade variations do occur, but this adds subtley to the products' natural beauty.

Each slate is individually produced by a skilled craftsman with the experience and expertise of a previous generation passed from father to son. Welsh slate is regarded as one of the best roofing materials in the world with the characteristics that will satisfy the most demanding application. This provides architects and specifiers with the confidence that, once properly laid, slate should stand the test of time.

Greaves Portmadog Slate has a natural blue-grey colour with a riven texture and is produced individually with chamfered edges. Natural markings and shade variations are the characteristics of a natural product. It is available in over 24 popular sizes.

Architectural slate products:

- Floor tiles in a variety of sizes for internal and external use
- Slate cladding for shop fascias
- Coping for garden walls and boundaries
- Pillared facing blocks for walling
- Crazy Paving
- Multi-coloured rustic slate for fireplaces and decorative walls
- Sawn slabs cut to individual requirements, eg hearths, shelving, mantles
- Slate engraving – housenames, company plaques
- Silk screening – company incentive and promotional gifts
- Tablemats and coasters

The former Llechwedd Slate Caverns underground slate workings extend deep below the ground and most consist of hugh caverns. Several of those near to the surface have been adapted to create one of the most popular visitor attractions in Wales. Some 7 million people have enjoyed a visit to Llechwedd since the attraction opened.

Part of a huge underground chamber, photographed in 1894

A steeply inclined working with slate extraction from the floor. The man farthest right holds a candle, which would never have lit the chamber. The photographer's magnesium strip lamps would have given the miners a previously unseen view of the workings.

A chamber worked out to the daylight

A staircase from 'the day' into the mine. Note the candle behind the man 2nd from the left

Left: The steeply sloping beds of slate meant many staircases were needed.
Note the rising main pumping water away

Here illuminated at the Oakeley mines, by the ingenuity of pioneering underground photographer J.C Burrows, this study illustrates the perils of working the enormous caverns by candlelight.

Worked out into the open (i.e. daylight), this is one of the spectacular chambers now experienced by tourists riding the Miners' Tramway through the Llechwedd workings. It has long been known as Choughs' Cavern, from the rare birds that have nested there year after year

Photographed by J.C. Burrow, in the Oakeley mines, this study shows an 86-feet long ladder assembled underground to facilitate roof inspections – usually by candlelight

Notice the ropes holding the ladder in place on this posed photograph.

Another view of an 86ft/26m long ladder and a roof inspection. The miner is holding the candle in one hand and his hammer in the other

Above: More posed scenes of miners at work. Note the small board supported on two pieces of iron rod, which supports the central figure of the photograph, plus the lit candle stuck in a piece of clay

Left: Rock drilling. Air-operated rock drills superceded hammers, the drill being turned a fraction between each blow of the hammer

A safety bridge crosses a working. It had iron supports (underneath), high skirting boards and a safety rail each side. Photographed at Llechwedd, where they originated

A miner pushes a fully loaded wagon. Horses were used on the main levels

This interesting scene shows both cable haulage (on the left) and a horse drawn wagon loaded with slate bound for the dressing mill

An additional view of the same spot. A chain spliced onto the cable is attached to the lead wagon on the cable way. As it was wound up, the cable was wrapped around a large drum on the surface (see page 18). A horse is bringing in another loaded wagon. On the right are three empties plus a large block of stone on a block wagon waiting to be hauled to the dressing floor

A three-legged derrick used for lifting heavy blocks of stone. Accidents were common when doing this until the Llechwedd mine manager invented a safety catch (see page 37)

Another derrick. Notice the repair on the leg and the two men beyond the derrick

Collecting rubble for disposal on the vast waste tips above ground

Not one of the men here is wearing a protective helmet, despite their availability in 1894, when photographed

The nearest of the men is working tied to a chain, whist another stands on a little wooden platform. The one in the middle steadies himself with one leg over a loop in a chain tied at each end to the bridge

The man in the foreground has the chain passing between his legs as on the previous photograph. The bridge was designed by C. Warren Roberts, manager at Llechwedd.

A driller in a low leading. Note the candle just above the drill

Above: A demonstration to Blaenau Ffestiniog mine managers of the Doering & Sachs pneumatic boring machine

A smaller hand held rock drill in use in the quarry

One of the old cable drums at the top of an incline. It would have been turned by steam power or if it was available, by water using a water wheel, which was cheaper. Sometimes water was brought long distances for this purpose

Men using the illegal Car Gwyllt (wild car) with the haulage cable beyond. Although these contraptions were popular at the end of the working day, the accident rate was high, causing them to be outlawed

Above: A horse drawn train of two block wagons and what appears to be a wagon of waste rock

Below: Block wagons had either three or four wooden bars or bearers. These were designed by Richard M Greaves of Llechwedd

Battery-electric locomotives (made by BEV) were introduced to Blaenau Ffestiniog in the 1920s to replace horses. The block carrying wagons, also seen on the previous page, were designed by Richard M.Greaves, in both three and four-bar versions

Busy 1894 production scenes at Llechwedd Slate Mines, Floor 5 (above) and floors 2 and 3 (below). Today's visitors will be able to identify the floor 2 buildings, most of which have been preserved in the heritage site

Floor 5 with slates awaiting dispatch

A steam-powered incline from Floor 5 at Llechwedd

A Ffestiniog Railway brake truck on floor 5 waiting to be loaded with slates for Porthmadog

On this incline, a waterwheel and a steam engine are being used for haulage. In this case it is likely that the water supply was subject to running too low to operate the wheel at certain times

Illegal man riding on a Blaenau Ffestiniog incline, showing a rubble wagon and a block carrier

An 1894 view of Floor 2, at Llechwedd

A Bagnall steam locomotive delivered to Llechwedd in 1890 can be seen in the above photograph, which also shows a water-balance incline in use. Slate was raised from below aboard a wheeled water tank, from which the water was gradually released to become counter-balanced by a full water wagon descending from above

Tipping slate waste. As can be seen on page 45, this is now finding a use on road schemes, as garden cover etc

The aerial waste removal system installed by Martyn Williams-Ellis, Llechwedd, a grandson of J.W Greaves

One of the many Llechwedd water wheels may be seen on the skyline of this picture

Splitting large slate blocks into more manageable size

Part of the Foty & Bowydd quarry, photographed in 1894 by G.J Williams, to show the opencast exploitation of supporting pillars from earlier mining activity. Foty & Bowydd now forms part of the Llechwedd complex

Slate stacking yards at Llechwedd State Mines. The little building near the right edge of the top picture was a row of pioneering self-flushing water closets, built over a stream which carried the problem away to someone else's territory! They may now be viewed by tourists. In the bottom scene, slate wagons are being filled prior to trans-shipment to Porthmadog harbour via the Ffestiniog Railway

One can but marvel at the length and strength of Canadian beams imported at Porthmadog, and hauled up the unsurfaced roads to Blaenau Ffestiniog, for roofing the slate mills shown in these 1894 photographs, taken by J.C. Burrows at Oakeley (below) and by C. Warren Roberts at Llechwedd (above)

Sawing slabs of slate. An enlargement of this view reveals people at the window on the far wall. The photographer would be an unusual sight, especially in rural communities, at that time (1894)

Another view of saw benches. Note the men sitting down beyond the benches and splitting slabs of stone to produce slates

These slabs of stone will be cut on the circular saw to the correct size of slate before they are split to create slates seen stacked in the background

Power for the circular saws came from the line-shafting worked by a horizontal axle and powered by steam or water power. The stone arrived on rail wagons, originally pulled by horse, later by a small battery-operated loco

Another huge dressing shed. Huge slabs of stone are being divided by chisels and large wooden mallets

A horse drawn wagon of stone, adjacent to a huge block being split into four pieces

The smaller blocks are then divided before being cut to the size of the desired slate

Slates being trimmed to size

Slate mining pioneer John Whitehead Greaves invented several machines for the industry but the only one for which he registered a patent was the slate dressing engine, shown on these pages. Originally they were hand-driven, like the one above, but were soon adapted for belt-drive from an overhead shaft driven by a water wheel. With embellishments for a new patent taken out by his son Richard M. Greaves, the Greaves dressing engine remains in use as standard equipment at all the world's slate mills. Today's machines are turned by electricity

Slates being stacked in the yard to await sale and shipment all around the world

A large slab about to be cut as required

Still preserved at Lechwedd Slate Caverns is one of the slate cutting knives used before the invention of the Greaves dressing engine

Visitors to the slate heritage mill at Llechwedd examine the sawing table invented by J.W. Greaves

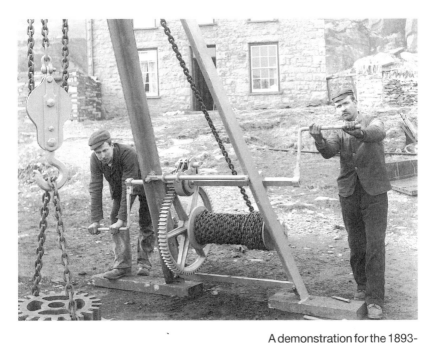

A demonstration for the 1893-94 Department Committee (a Government Commission) of the safety winch devised by Charles Warren Roberts for underground derricks used to lift newly quarried blocks. It had a mechanism to stop the chain from running back. Many accidents were avoided by its adoption. Its inventor was the Llechwedd mine manager

John Whitehead Greaves (1807-80) founded the family slate business in 1836, opening up Llechwedd a decade later

In 1870 John Whitehead Greaves, founder of Lechwedd Slate Mines, built himself a handsome house at the entrance, well away from the stench of the town. He called it Plas Weunydd and it now serves as the headquarters of the family company bearing his name

A modern view from Plas Weunydd. The building on the skyline, top left, is Floor 7 Mill, where roofing slates are made. Below it, and to the right, is the Floor 5 Mill complex, and immediately below that is Floor 3 Mill. The tree in the right foreground conceals the modern tourist heritage site

The carriage takes today's visitors down Britain's steepest passenger railway, with a gradient of 1:1.8, at Llechwedd Slate Caverns. Its passengers have included Princess Margaret, the Duchess of Gloucester and Crown Prince Naruhito of Japan. Visitors alight for a walking tour through some of the earliest underground workings, now enhanced with ten sound and light programmes that unfold the social life of a Victorian miner

The gradual revelation, by unfolding lighting sequences, of the hugh lake two floors beneth the suface at Llechwedd Slate Caverns is one of the most dramatic episodes of a modern tour. The lake has been used as a set for two Hollywood films *(Prince Valiant* and *Black Cauldron)* and its shoreline has become a popular wedding venue

More than six million visitors have ridden on the miners' tramway, seen here in Chough's Cavern

New 400KW turbine at the Pant yr afon powerhouse generating hydro renewable electricty for the national grid using water from 3 reservoirs sited on the 2000-acre property. The powerhouse originally generated power for the quarry's needs from 1904 to 2003. It was commissioned in November 2007

Modern day open cast quarrying showing the exposed underground chambers, a 45 tonne excavator and dumper truck

Two images of modern day open cast quarrying showing the exposed underground chambers

Modern day slate sawing and polishing operations in the cutting shed

The cutting shed with an electric saw and water to suppress dust

View of a wall clad with Llechwedd slate blocks. The image shows small section of a large residential programme in Swansea marina, a contract that took 18 months to complete

Excavation from an existing slate tip to process crushed slate primarily for road construction purposes. This process is classes as secondary aggregate and has environmental benefits because existing stock piles are used instead of opening new quarries

Selection of roof finishes using Llechwedd blue-grey slate. Roofing is our primary product but slate for other architectural uses is becoming popular.

Left: Innovative use of slate used in the construction of a twisting tower feature at the end of the M32 at Cabot Circus, Bristol. Over 50,000 pieces of slate were used in this project.

Right: Slate provides a durable material for steps

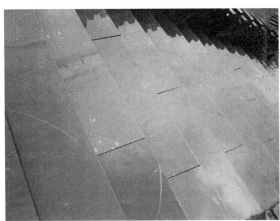

Above & Left: Llechwedd Slate Caverns shop products, showing the versatility of slate to meet a variety of modern needs

Published by

Landmark Publishing

The Oaks, Moor Farm Road West, Ashbourne, Derbyshire, DE6 1HD
Tel: (01335) 347349 Fax: (01335) 347303
www.landmarkpublishing.co.uk

ISBN 13: 978-1-84306-484-8

© Lindsey Porter 2009

British Library Cataloguing in Publication Data: a catalogue record for this book is
available from the British Library.

Printed by: Athenaeum Press Limited, Gateshead

Designed by: Michelle Prost

Front Cover: Slate splitting and dressing at Llechwedd in 1894,
photographed by C.W Roberts

Page 1: One can marvel at the length and strenth of Canadian beams imported at
Portmadog and hauled up the unsurfaced roads to Blaenau Ffestiniog for roofing the
slate mills shown in these 1894 photgraphs,photograph by J.C Burrow at Oakeley

Back Cover Top: Llechwedd dressing floor

Back Cover Botton left: A demonstration to Bleanau Ffestiniog mine managers of the
Doering & Sachs pneumatic boring machine

Back Cover Bottom Right: Modern slate ready for dispatch,
photograph by Dave King